W9-APK-231

TRY NOT TO LAUGH CHALLENGE™

WOULD YOU RATHER?

Valentine's Day

EDITION

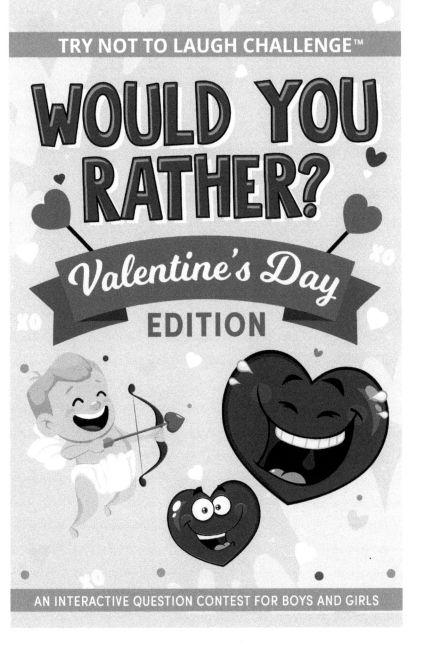

AN INTERACTIVE QUESTION CONTEST FOR BOYS AND GIRLS

Try Not To Laugh Challenge
BONUS PLAY

Join our Joke Club and get the Bonus Play PDF!

Simply send us an email to:

➤ **TNTLPublishing@gmail.com** ◄

and you will get the following:

- 10 Hilarious Would You Rather Questions
- An entry in our Monthly Giveaway of a $50 Amazon Gift card!

We draw a new winner each month and will contact you via email!

Good luck!

Welcome to
The Try Not to Laugh Challenge
Would You Rather?
VALENTINE'S EDITION

RULES:

• Face your opponent and decide who is 'Player 1' and 'Player 2'.

• Starting with 'Player 1', read the Would You Rather question aloud and pick an answer. The same player will then explain why they chose that answer in the most hilarious or wacky way possible!

• If the reason makes 'Player 2' laugh, then a laugh point is scored!

• Take turns going back and forth, then mark your total laugh points at the end of each round!

• Whoever gets the most laugh points is officially crowned the 'Laugh Master'!

• If ending with a tie, finish with the Tie-Breaker round for WINNER TAKES ALL!

Most importantly, have fun and be SILLY! 😄

CRAZY COREY

REMEMBER, these scenarios listed in the book are solely for fun and games! Please do NOT attempt any of the crazy scenarios in this book.

ROUND

1

Player 1

(DON'T FORGET TO EXPLAIN YOUR ANSWERS!)

Would you rather have a pet spider that is trained to tap dance OR have Cupid teach you all his love spells?

Laugh Point_____/1

Would you rather have jelly beans for teeth OR Twizzlers for hair?

Laugh Point_____/1

10

Player 1

Would you rather find the fountain of youth and be able to stay young forever, OR be the first one to meet Cupid in real life?

Laugh Point_____/1

Would you rather be able to experience Valentine's Day everyday OR skip Valentine's Day every year?

Laugh Point_____/1

Player 2

Would you rather your shadow be a cute baby Cupid that helps you fly OR a beautiful unicorn that you can ride?

Laugh Point____/1

Would you rather all your food be a shade of pink and red OR every piece of clothing you own be a shade of green and purple?

Laugh Point____/1

12

Player 2

Would you rather be able to shoot arrows and make people fall in love, like Cupid OR shoot arrows and make people fart on command?

Laugh Point____/1

Would you rather be a wizard who can make chocolate with the snap of a finger OR a vampire who only eats cotton candy?

Laugh Point____/1

13

Add up your scores and record them below!

Player  /4

ROUND TOTAL

Player ❷ /4

ROUND TOTAL

_____

ROUND CHAMPION

Player 1

Would you rather only be able to eat dessert that doesn't contain chocolate OR only eat chocolate, but never be able to eat other desserts?

Laugh Point_____ /1

Would you rather live in a treehouse with no bathroom OR live on a boat without a TV?

Laugh Point_____ /1

Player 1

Would you rather turn everything you touch (including people) into a box of chocolates, OR turn everything you see (including people) into Red Hots?

Laugh Point____/1

Would you rather have to kiss with your forehead OR have to hug with your legs?

Laugh Point____/1

Player ❤2

Would you rather walk across the Grand Canyon on a bridge made of chocolate bars OR swing across it on a rope made of Twizzlers?

Laugh Point____/1

Would you rather sleep in a bed of half-melted chocolate OR have half-melted gummy worms stuck in your hair during school?

Laugh Point____/1

Player 2

Would you rather be best friends with Cupid, even though he shoots you with a different love arrow every day OR the Tooth Fairy, even though she never gives you money when your teeth fall out?

Laugh Point_____/1

Would you rather pick 100 roses, but get pricked by thorns every time OR have to eat the actual box to get to the chocolates inside?

Laugh Point_____/1

Add up your scores and record them below!

Player  **1** — /4
ROUND TOTAL

Player **2** — /4
ROUND TOTAL

_____

ROUND CHAMPION

ROUND

3

Player 💙 1

Would you rather be trapped inside the mind of a baby doll for the rest of your life, OR be stuck inside a toy race car that is your dog's favorite chew toy?

Laugh Point____/1

Would you rather be able to read your pet's mind OR your crush's mind?

Laugh Point____/1

22

Player 1

Would you rather travel through space and come back 10 years older OR stay on Earth and remain the same age forever?

Laugh Point____/1

Would you rather listen to a love story told by a mysterious cat, OR random stories from the world's most ancient tree?

Laugh Point____/1

Player ♥2

(DON'T FORGET TO EXPLAIN YOUR ANSWERS!)

Would you rather have Cupid's wings, but be unable to fly higher than 50 feet OR a unicorn's horn, but no magical powers other than farting sparkles?

Laugh Point_____/1

Would you rather bounce from place to place on streets made of trampolines OR be able to travel anywhere by zip line?

Laugh Point_____/1

Player 2

Would you rather constantly be running from Cupid's arrows OR have to be Cupid's body guard 24/7?

Laugh Point____ /1

Would you rather be shot out of a circus cannon into a pool of sticky, delicious marshmallows OR a pool of melted chocolate frosting?

Laugh Point____ /1

Add up your scores and record them below!

Player  1 _____ /4
ROUND TOTAL

Player 2 _____ /4
ROUND TOTAL

_____
ROUND
CHAMPION

ROUND

4

Player ❤ 1

Would you rather be the personal trainer for an overweight koala OR the anger management coach for an irritable chimpanzee?

Laugh Point_____/1

Would you rather try the sourest gummy worms of all time OR try the spiciest Red Hots there ever was?

Laugh Point_____/1

Player 1

(DON'T FORGET TO EXPLAIN YOUR ANSWERS!)

Would you rather be a trapeze artist that jumps from tall heights OR a lion tamer at the circus?

Laugh Point_____/1

Would you rather only be able to pick your pet's name by randomly selecting candy heart phrases OR only be able to name your pet after emojis?

Laugh Point_____/1

Player 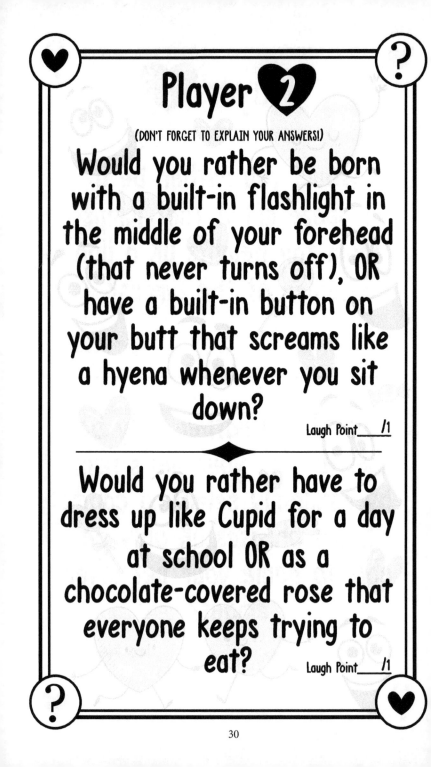 2

(DON'T FORGET TO EXPLAIN YOUR ANSWERS!)

Would you rather be born with a built-in flashlight in the middle of your forehead (that never turns off), OR have a built-in button on your butt that screams like a hyena whenever you sit down?

Laugh Point____/1

Would you rather have to dress up like Cupid for a day at school OR as a chocolate-covered rose that everyone keeps trying to eat?

Laugh Point____/1

Player ❤2

Would you rather drink 10 Smarties milkshakes OR 10 candy heart sandwiches?

Laugh Point____/1

Would you rather be hollow inside and be able to collect money like a piggy bank, but you have to break something to get any money out OR be able to make your favorite things appear, but you have to be hit like a piñata for it to happen?

Laugh Point____/1

Add up your scores and record them below!

Player  /4

ROUND TOTAL

Player ❤2 /4

ROUND TOTAL

ROUND
CHAMPION

ROUND

5

Player 1

(DON'T FORGET TO EXPLAIN YOUR ANSWERS!)

Would you rather change your first name to 'Supercalifragilisticexpiali-docious' OR change your last name to 'ABCDEFGHIJKLMNOPQRSTUVWXYZ'?

Laugh Point____/1

Would you rather wake up one morning with tiny wings like Fairy Godmother's OR huge antlers like Bullwinkle?

Laugh Point____/1

34

Player 1

Would you rather live in the past as a Greek god/goddess OR live 300 years in the future as an everyday person with a robot best friend?

Laugh Point_____ /1

Would you rather have to change baby Cupid's diaper everyday OR have to eat a chocolate-filled cherry before every word you speak?

Laugh Point_____ /1

Player 2

(DON'T FORGET TO EXPLAIN YOUR ANSWERS!)

Would you rather have a pancake breakfast with Cupid OR a buffet dinner with the Easter Bunny?

Laugh Point____ /1

Would you rather have a pocket-sized magician to perform tricks whenever you want OR have a pocket-sized pet dragon that roars whenever you are in danger?

Laugh Point____ /1

Player ♥2

Would you rather have a mustache made out of sour gummy worms OR a hat made out of fruit snacks?

Laugh Point____ /1

Would you rather ride a roller coaster that goes through the center of the Earth OR ride a waterslide that starts on the moon?

Laugh Point____ /1

Add up your scores and record them below!

Player

/4
ROUND TOTAL

Player **2**

/4
ROUND TOTAL

ROUND CHAMPION

ROUND

6

Player 1

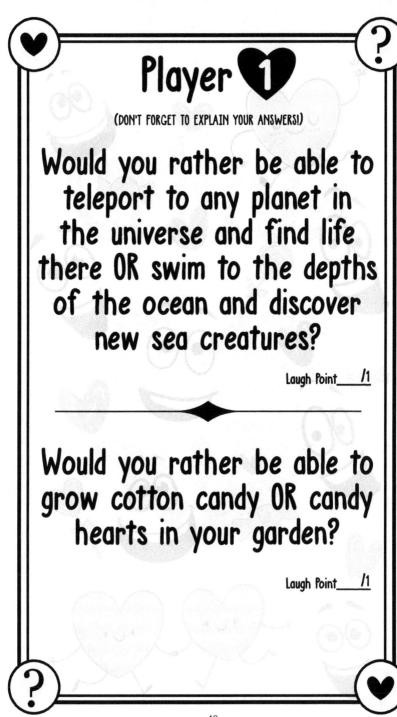

(DON'T FORGET TO EXPLAIN YOUR ANSWERS!)

Would you rather be able to teleport to any planet in the universe and find life there OR swim to the depths of the ocean and discover new sea creatures?

Laugh Point_____/1

Would you rather be able to grow cotton candy OR candy hearts in your garden?

Laugh Point_____/1

Player 1

Would you rather be able to walk up walls like a lizard OR have wings on your back and fly like a dragonfly?

Laugh Point____/1

Would you rather have to read a love poem in front of your entire class OR tell your crush that you want them to be your Valentine?

Laugh Point____/1

Player

Would you rather be able to bring balloon animals to life OR give stuffed animals the ability to talk?

Laugh Point_____ /1

Would you rather talk to an old tree who could tell you stories from millions of years ago OR talk to a dolphin who could give you tours of the oceans?

Laugh Point_____ /1

Player 2

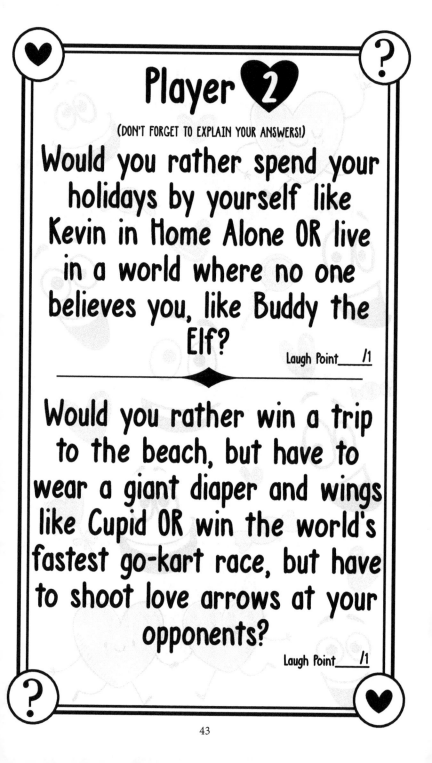

(DON'T FORGET TO EXPLAIN YOUR ANSWERS!)

Would you rather spend your holidays by yourself like Kevin in Home Alone OR live in a world where no one believes you, like Buddy the Elf?

Laugh Point_____ /1

Would you rather win a trip to the beach, but have to wear a giant diaper and wings like Cupid OR win the world's fastest go-kart race, but have to shoot love arrows at your opponents?

Laugh Point_____ /1

Add up your scores and record them below!

Player

ROUND TOTAL

Player 2 /4

ROUND TOTAL

ROUND CHAMPION

ROUND

7

Player  ❤ **1**

Would you rather jump across the Grand Canyon on a unicorn OR walk across it on a Nerds rope?

Laugh Point_____ /1

Would you rather ski down a 500-foot slope made of the best chocolate you've ever tasted OR go down a 500-foot waterslide full of Kool-Aid?

Laugh Point_____ /1

Player 1

(DON'T FORGET TO EXPLAIN YOUR ANSWERS!)

Would you rather live where endless amounts of dog hair fall from the sky OR live where all grass is made of fur balls from a cat?

Laugh Point_____/1

Would you rather be the King/Queen of your classroom's Valentine's Day party OR be the one that gets the most Valentine's Day cards and candy?

Laugh Point_____/1

Player 2

(DON'T FORGET TO EXPLAIN YOUR ANSWERS!)

Would you rather have a shirt that makes you really strong, but it always smells like roses OR shoes that make you really fast, but they always leak grape juice?

Laugh Point____ /1

Would you rather have a hole in your mattress that magically transports you to an alternate universe OR a coat that transforms you into different people?

Laugh Point____ /1

Player ❤ 2

Would you rather be able to stick your hand inside your TV and pull out items on commercials OR have taste-a-vision and be able to taste any food that is on the TV?

Laugh Point_____/1

Would you rather be the only cat in a rock band of dogs OR the only peacock in a flock of ducks?

Laugh Point_____/1

Add up your scores and record them below!

Player

/4
ROUND TOTAL

Player

/4
ROUND TOTAL

_____

ROUND CHAMPION

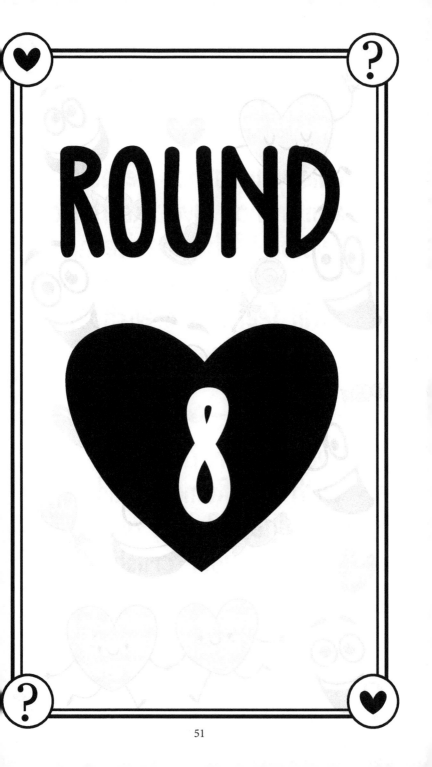

ROUND

8

Player 1

Would you rather be able to swim in hot lava like it was water OR be outside no matter how cold it is and still feel warm without layering up?

Laugh Point____/1

Would you rather play tag with the Roman goddess, Aphrodite, OR hide-and-seek with your crush?

Laugh Point____/1

Player 1

Would you rather wake up to see your body covered with pink fur OR fluffy red feathers?

Laugh Point_____/1

Would you rather surf a cascading wave of blue raspberry Gatorade OR climb a giant 100-foot chocolate building?

Laugh Point_____/1

Player 2

Would you rather have a ceiling fan that rained rose petals when you turned it on OR a shower that produces your favorite soda rather than water?

Laugh Point____/1

Would you rather receive a rose from everyone in school, OR be able to give a rose to everyone in school?

Laugh Point____/1

54

Player 💙2💙

Would you rather help Cupid by carrying around his bow and arrows OR help the Tooth Fairy by building a Caribbean vacation home out of teeth?

Laugh Point____/1

Would you rather fall into a hole on a mini-golf course and land in a universe where everything is made of chocolate OR jump into a bottomless pit that leads to jelly bean land?

Laugh Point____/1

Add up your scores and record them below!

Player

/4
ROUND TOTAL

Player **2**

/4
ROUND TOTAL

ROUND
CHAMPION

ROUND

9

Player ❤ 1

(DON'T FORGET TO EXPLAIN YOUR ANSWERS!)

Would you rather be able to travel to Italy with your family for a month OR travel to Paris with your crush for a week?

Laugh Point_____/1

Would you rather Valentine's Day be about love and pizza OR love and tacos?

Laugh Point_____/1

Player 1

Would you rather have the ability to breathe fire OR the ability to breathe underwater for 20 minutes?

Laugh Point_____ /1

Would you rather live in the world of 'Frozen', but you have to dance with the Duke of Wesselton every day OR live in 'How to Train Your Dragon', but you can't train any dragons?

Laugh Point_____ /1

59

Player 2

Would you rather your school mascot come alive and challenge you to a duel OR find out your school nurse is a ninja, but only after she attacks you?

Laugh Point_____/1

Would you rather be able to only speak for an hour a day OR have to talk non-stop all day long, but only speak in love poems?

Laugh Point_____/1

Player ❤ 2

Would you rather brush your teeth with magical toothpaste that turns your teeth into different colors OR use a candy toothbrush that never runs out?

Laugh Point____ /1

Would you rather have the job of putting a sneaky, disappearing genie back in its bottle OR pretending to redecorate the evil witch's castle while waiting for Hansel and Gretel to arrive?

Laugh Point____ /1

Add up your scores and record them below!

Player

/4

ROUND TOTAL

Player

/4

ROUND TOTAL

_____

ROUND CHAMPION

ROUND

10

Player ❤ ①

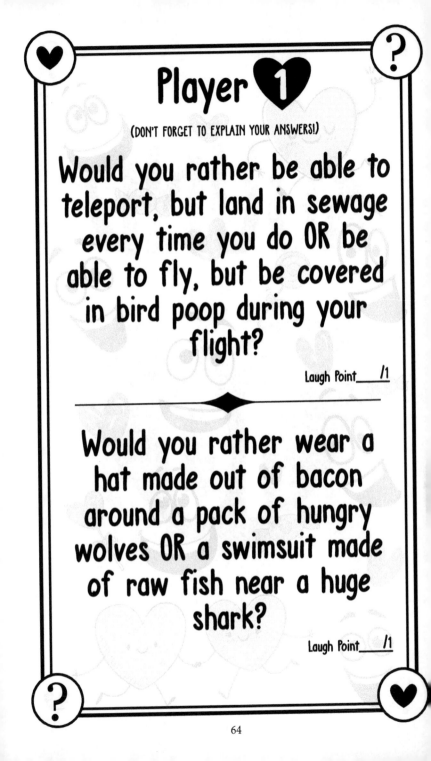

(DON'T FORGET TO EXPLAIN YOUR ANSWERS!)

Would you rather be able to teleport, but land in sewage every time you do OR be able to fly, but be covered in bird poop during your flight?

Laugh Point____/1

Would you rather wear a hat made out of bacon around a pack of hungry wolves OR a swimsuit made of raw fish near a huge shark?

Laugh Point____/1

Player 1

(DON'T FORGET TO EXPLAIN YOUR ANSWERS!)

Would you rather be friends with Cupid, but no one one can see him except you OR be Cupid, but get no credit for helping people fall in love?

Laugh Point____/1

Would you rather be able to change into any animal OR change into any other human?

Laugh Point____/1

Player 2

Would you rather go to a zombie circus where the acts attack OR go to a magic show where the magician turns the audience into hungry lions?

Laugh Point____ /1

Would you rather fight a giant Cupid, who can grow as tall as the Empire State Building OR an army of leprechauns with the strength of Thor?

Laugh Point____ /1

Player  2

(DON'T FORGET TO EXPLAIN YOUR ANSWERS!)

Would you rather be able to turn invisible when you dance the Cupid Shuffle OR be able to breathe underwater, but only when you flap your arms like a chicken?

Laugh Point_____/1

Would you rather have imaginary things become reality (even scary things) OR have the ability to make real things disappear?

Laugh Point_____/1

Add up your scores and record them below!

Player

/4
ROUND TOTAL

Player

/4
ROUND TOTAL

ROUND CHAMPION

Add up all your points from each round.
The PLAYER with the most points is crowned
The Laugh Master!

In the event of a tie, continue to Round 11
for the Tie-Breaker Round!

Player  ❤ 1

_____
GRAND TOTAL

Player ❤ 2

_____
GRAND TOTAL

_____

The
Laugh Master

ROUND 11

TIE-BREAKER
(WINNER TAKES ALL!)

Player

(DON'T FORGET TO EXPLAIN YOUR ANSWERS!)

Would you rather swim with a mermaid in a sea of the best hot chocolate OR ride a unicorn across a rainbow made of rock candy?

Laugh Point_____ /1

Would you rather eat all of your Valentine's Day candy in one sitting OR eat it over the course of a week, but have to wear Cupid footie pajamas every time you eat a piece?

Laugh Point_____ /1

Player 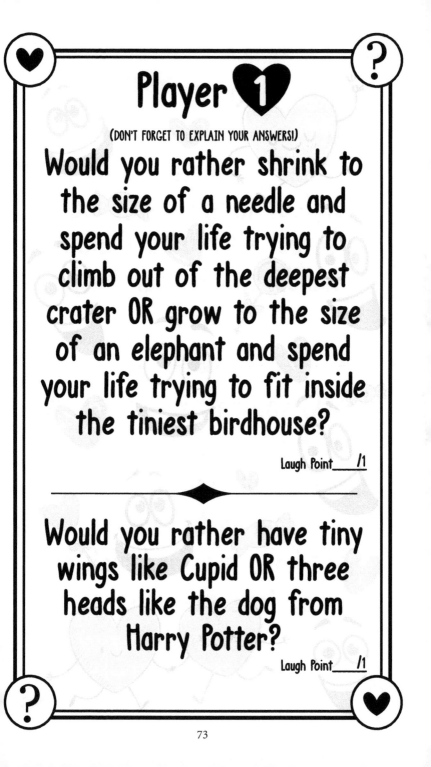 1

Would you rather shrink to the size of a needle and spend your life trying to climb out of the deepest crater OR grow to the size of an elephant and spend your life trying to fit inside the tiniest birdhouse?

Laugh Point_____ /1

Would you rather have tiny wings like Cupid OR three heads like the dog from Harry Potter?

Laugh Point_____ /1

Player 2

Would you rather find a Bigfoot footprint at your nearest park OR a Bigfoot handprint on your back door?

Laugh Point_____/1

Would you rather be able to shoot a bow and arrow and make people fall in love, like Cupid OR be Santa's right-hand man and pick out what toys everyone gets each year?

Laugh Point_____/1

Player 2

Would you rather swim in a pool full of hot sauce with your eyes open OR roll down a hill while locked in a barrel with 25 scorpions?

Laugh Point_____/1

Would you rather blow gummy bears out of your nostrils, instead of snot OR shoot Twizzlers from your eyes, like lasers?

Laugh Point_____/1

Add up all your points from Round 11.
The PLAYER with the most points is crowned
The Laugh Master!

Player 1 ___/4
ROUND TOTAL

Player 2 ___/4
ROUND TOTAL

_____
The
Laugh Master

Check out our

Visit our Amazon Store at:

other joke books!

www.Amazon.com/author/CrazyCorey

CPSIA information can be obtained
at www.ICGtesting.com
Printed in the USA
BVHW042100210122
626782BV00004B/406